SAILOR JACK SERIES

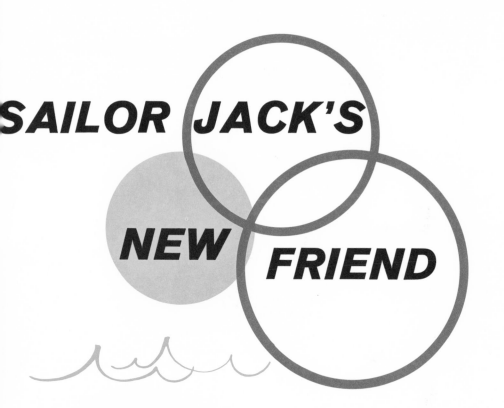

SAILOR JACK'S NEW FRIEND

by Selma and Jack Wassermann

pictures by Don Loehle

Benefic Press Chicago

Publishing Division of Beckley-Cardy Company

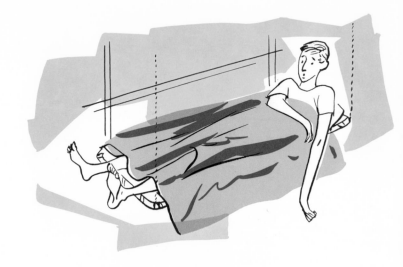

CONTENTS

Copyright 1960 by Benefic Press
All Rights Reserved
Printed in the United States of America

Library of Congress
Number 60-9014

The New Man

Sailor Jack is a radio man
on an atomic submarine.
His ship is the SHARK.
Here he is with Bluebell.
Jack does much work.
Some days he must work
for a long, long time.

This is
Captain White.

One day, Captain White said, "Men, we are going to get a new man.

He will help us with our work."

It was the day for the new man
to come onto the ship.

All the sailors wanted to see him.

Then Sailor Jack said,
"Look, here comes a man now."

"And what a man he is!"
said one of the sailors.

"What a big, big man he is!"
said all the sailors on the SHARK.
When the new man came
onto the ship, Jack went to him.

"My name
is Jack,"
he said.
"What is
your name?"

"My name is George,"
said the man.

Then he looked down.

"But I am called Beanpole,
too," he said.

All the sailors laughed.

"Beanpole!" they said.

"That is a good name for you."

Beanpole laughed a little, too.

Beanpole and Captain White

Jack took Beanpole to see
Captain White.

"Here is
the new man,"
said Jack.

"Good!" said
Captain White.

Then Captain White looked up.

"My! My!" he said.

"Are you the new man?"

"Yes, sir," said Beanpole.

"But you are much too big
to be on a submarine!"
said Captain White.

"I am a good sailor, sir,"
said Beanpole.

Captain White
looked at Beanpole
for a long time.
Then he said,
"You will be
a big man
on a little ship.
You could run
into trouble.
We will have
to see."

Then Beanpole went
with Captain White.

"I want you to work here,"
said Captain White.

"You will come here
in the morning."

"Yes, sir," said Beanpole.

"I can do good work here."

The SHARK sailors liked Beanpole.
They laughed at the things he said.
Jack and Bluebell laughed, too.
Beanpole was happy on his new ship.

Where Will Beanpole Sleep?

Then it was time to sleep.

Jack and Bluebell went to sleep.

Beanpole had trouble.

He could not go to sleep.

"Captain White
said I was too big
for this ship.
I am too big
to sleep here!"
said Beanpole.
"Bluebell, we must
help Beanpole,"
said Jack.

Bluebell jumped
down here.

"Help Beanpole!
Help Beanpole!"
she said.

"Good, Bluebell!"
said Jack.

"That is what
we will do."

"What will
you do?"
Beanpole said.

17

"See!" said Jack.

"Now you can sleep."

Beanpole said, "Jack and Bluebell,
you are my good friends."

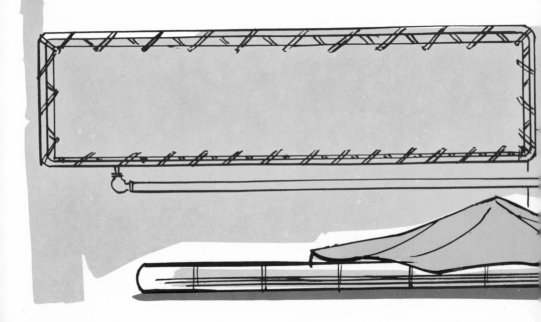

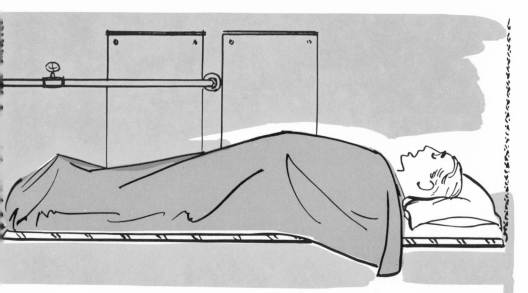

"Good friends!" said Bluebell.
Then they all went to sleep.
This time, Beanpole went
to sleep, too.

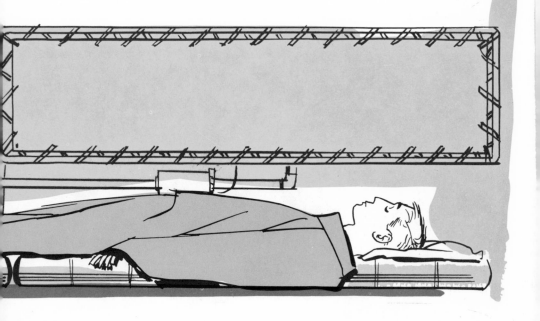

Beanpole Has Trouble

In the morning, the men went
to work again.
Jack went
to the radio.

Beanpole went
to his work.

The sailors
helped Beanpole
learn his work.

Beanpole worked
and worked.

"When we dive,
you work here,"
said one sailor.
"Then you must
work fast."

Soon Captain White called,
"Dive! Dive!"
The sailors jumped up.
They went to work fast.
Beanpole worked fast, too!

There was trouble for Beanpole.
He did good, fast work,
but the men could hear him
all over the ship.

Captain White saw Beanpole.

"This is not good,"
said Captain White.

"You must learn that you are
on a little ship."

"Yes, sir," said Beanpole.

"What is this?"
said Jack.

"I had trouble,"
said Beanpole.

The sailors laughed and said,

"We could hear you all over the ship!"

"I have trouble when I work fast,
but I will learn," said Beanpole.

When it was
time to dive
again, Beanpole
did not run
into things.
But he could not work fast.
"Work faster, Beanpole!"
said the sailors.

"I will get into trouble again
if I work fast," said Beanpole.

Captain White
came in.

"I did not hear
Beanpole," he said.

"But that was
not a good dive.
You men must
work much faster,"
said Captain White.

"I was the one that did not
work fast, Captain,"
said Beanpole.

"But I did not have trouble."

Captain White said, "We must do
a fast dive in the morning.

No one must hear us."

Then he looked at Beanpole.

"You must not work then," he said.

The SHARK
Gets Away

Captain White
said, "Men, other
ships are coming
to find us.

But they will
have something
like a radio
that can find
the SHARK
under the water,"
said Captain White.

"They must not
find us!"

The men worked fast.

All the men worked
but Beanpole.

Down went
the SHARK.
It went
far down.
The other
ships came.

"Not too fast,"
said Captain White.
"They will hear us
if we go too fast."

34

The SHARK went on.

Then Captain White said, "Stop!

They are over us now."

The men stopped working.

No one jumped.

No one ran.

The men on the other ships
looked for the SHARK.
They looked and looked.
They could not find it.

The men
on the other ships
said, "The SHARK
is not here.
We must go on
to look for it."

Down in the SHARK,

the men looked at Jack.

"Where are they?" said a sailor.

"Shh!" said Jack.

"Shh!" said Bluebell.

The sailor stopped talking.

Time went on.

Then Jack said,

"They are going away!

They did not find us!"

Captain White was happy.

"You are good men!" he said.

"The SHARK is a good ship."

"Good ship!" said Bluebell.

"Ding-ding!"

When the SHARK
went on again,
a sailor ran
to Captain White.
He said, "The SHARK
is in trouble.
It will not go
where we want
it to go!"

"Up!" said
Captain White.
"Go up fast!"

Trouble for the SHARK

The SHARK
came up fast.
"Come!" said
Captain White.
"We must
have a look."
Up went
Captain White
and the men.

They looked
and looked
for the trouble.
"There it is!"
said Jack.
"Yes," said
Captain White.
"I can see
it, too."

A sailor said,
"This is work
for me."

He went to work.

Soon the sailor
said, "I can not
get to it.

It is too far
away for me."

45

"What will we do now?"
said Captain White.

"With this trouble, we cannot get
the SHARK back.

We must do this work here
and now."

Then a sailor said,

"Where is Beanpole?"

This is not too far away for him!"

"Yes!" said Captain White.

"Beanpole can help us."

"Help! Help!" said Bluebell.

No one laughed at her.

This was no time to laugh.

"Beanpole!
Come here,"
said Jack.
"You must help!"

Beanpole saw what
he had to do.
"I can do it,"
he said.

Jack and some other sailors
helped Beanpole.

"Down a little," said Beanpole.

"You are going over too far,"
said Jack.

"No! No! Go on," said Beanpole.

Down a little
went Beanpole.
"Now I can
do the work!"
said Beanpole.

Beanpole worked and worked.

All the men looked down

at Beanpole.

They could not look away.

Beanpole worked on and on.

Then Beanpole said,
"Help me up now.
I did all that I could do."
They helped Beanpole up.

"Down into the submarine, men!"
said Captain White.

"We must see where the SHARK
will go now."

The men went

to work.

Soon the submarine was going.

"So far, so good!"

said Captain White.

"Now we must go faster."

Faster and faster went the SHARK.

The SHARK was not in trouble now!

Captain White looked at Beanpole.

"Good work, Beanpole," he said.

"No one but you could do it.

It is good to have a big man

on a submarine."

"Good work, Beanpole!"

said all the sailors, too.

"But there is not work
like that all the time,"
said Beanpole.

"I want to do good work
on the SHARK all the time.
But I can not do it."

Captain White could see
that Beanpole was not happy.

Work for Beanpole

"There must be something
Beanpole can do on this ship,"
said Captain White.

Then Jack said,
"Captain, let
Beanpole help me."

"He could work
with me and have
no trouble at all,"
said Jack.

Captain White looked at Jack.

He looked at Beanpole, too.

Then he said, "Yes, Jack.

You work and work.

You must have help.

I will let Beanpole help you."

Now Beanpole was happy.

Jack and Bluebell were happy, too.

Beanpole did good work for Jack.

He did not run into trouble again.

"We are happy that you are
on the SHARK with us,"
Jack and the other sailors said.
"I am happy that you men are
my good friends," said Beanpole.

"Friend! Friend!" said Bluebell.

Beanpole laughed at Bluebell.

"And you, too, Bluebell!" he said.

"You are all my good friends!"

Vocabulary

The total number of words in this book is 114. Of these, 9 are first-grade words and appear below in roman type; 10 are above first-grade level and appear below in italic type. The numbers indicate the pages on which the words first appear.

The remaining 95 words are below first-grade level and have not been listed on this page.

atomic 5	hear 23	other 31
	if 27	*radio* 5
dive 21		
does 5		*sailors* 7
	learn 21	*ship* 5
	long 5	*sir* 11
far 34		
		submarine 5
faster 28	men 6	
friends 19	much 5	*trouble* 12